Joseph Bettey was formerly Reader in Local History at the University of Bristol. He has been interested in the history of Dorset for many years, and has contributed numerous articles to the *Proceedings* of Dorset Natural History and Archaeological Society, and to other publications. His research has included work on records relating to historic agriculture, rural society and church life in the county, and among his numerous books are: *Dorset* (1974), *Rural Life in Wessex* (1977 & 1987), *The Landscape of Wessex* (1980), *Wessex from AD 1000* (1986), *Church and Parish* (1987), *Suppresion of the Monasteries in the West Country* (1989), *Estates and the English Countryside* (1993) and *Man and the Land* (with Jo Draper) (1996).

Following page
Hay harvest at Toogoods Farm, Marnhull in about 1914.
The heavy work of lifting the hay up to the rick was greatly helped by the horse-powered hay pole and grab which are shown here on top of the waggon.

DISCOVER DORSET

FARMING

J.H.BETTEY

THE DOVECOTE PRESS

Dorset Horn ewes.

First published in 2000 by The Dovecote Press Ltd
Stanbridge, Wimborne, Dorset BH21 4JD

ISBN 1 874336 69 5

Series designed by Humphrey Stone

Typeset in Monotype Sabon
Printed and bound by Baskerville Press, Salisbury, Wiltshire

A CIP catalogue record for this book is available
from the British Library

CONTENTS

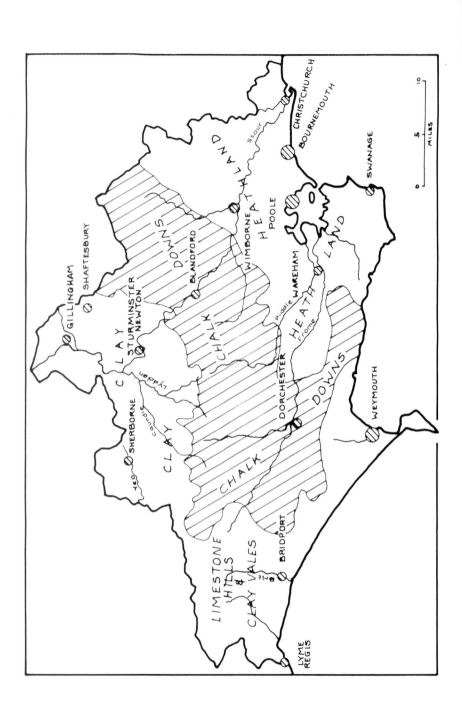

MEDIEVAL FARMING

Farming has always been by far the most important economic activity in Dorset, and until recently most people in the county were either directly or indirectly dependent upon it. Many parts of the landscape, especially on the chalk downs, bear evidence of the activities of prehistoric farmers. Farming was widely practised in Dorset during the Neolithic period, and has thus been carried on in the county for over six thousand years. Not until more recent times, however, is detailed documentary evidence available. The major features of farming in the county were already discernable when the Domesday Survey was compiled in 1086. Dorset is remarkable for the variety of its geology and scenery, and although the Domesday Survey is concerned with taxation and not specifically with farming or the landscape, the three distinctive regions of Dorset were obviously recognised by the compilers. The chalk downlands which occupy almost half of the county are depicted in the Survey as well-populated, with strings of villages along the length of the river valleys, numerous mills and with far-spreading upland pastures. This was the region in which until the later nineteenth century farming was to be based on the twin pillars of sheep and corn; where large sheep flocks were fed all day on the downs and at night were folded on the arable land, enriching it with their dung, and enabling good crops of wheat and barley to be grown on the thin chalkland soil.

The acid soils of the heathland which occupy the south-east of Dorset continue to present a challenge to farmers. This area is shown in the Domesday Survey to have less than half the population of other parts of Dorset. Here there was little arable land and farmers survived by raising sheep, cattle, or the free-ranging ponies which many centuries later Thomas Hardy in *The Return of the Native* was to describe as 'heath-croppers'. Heathland farmers often also engaged in other occupations such as quarrying, clay or peat digging, salt production

The complex pattern of irregularly-shaped fields near Whitchurch Canonicorum, bounded by massive banks, with narrow winding lanes joining the isolated farms. This landscape is the result of slow, arduous clearance in this once thickly-wooded area.

along the coast, or fishing and wild-fowling.

Quite different are the well-wooded clay vales of the north and west of the county. Here the Domesday Survey records numerous well-populated villages together with many scattered hamlets and farms. In the west many of these farms remain, and are still surrounded by the small, irregularly-shaped fields created by the unremitting toil of countless generations of farmers. In 1086 this was already a region of pasture and stock-rearing. The large manor of Sherborne was recorded as one of the most prosperous in the county, with nearly seventy plough teams and twelve mills. These are of course broad classifications, and Dorset's complex geology means that there are many sub-regions. For example, the soils of the Isle of Purbeck differ from those of the surrounding heath; the limestone hills of west Dorset

The large monastic barns, like this example at Abbotsbury, leave no doubt
of the large quantities of produce which had to be stored. They provide
striking evidence of the productivity of the monastic estates.

An example of a medieval sheep fold from the Luttrell Psalter.
The sheep are confined within wattle hurdles, enriching the
arable land with their dung; they are also providing milk.

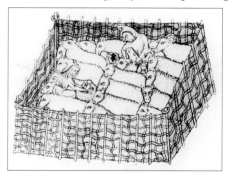

are quite distinct from the clay vales; and there are many places in the
chalklands where clay-with-flints cover the chalk, providing a
different soil and supporting a richer vegetation.

The Exeter version of the Domesday Survey also lists the livestock
kept on some Dorset manors. This reveals the overwhelming
importance of sheep in Dorset farming: more than 22,000 are recorded; many of them kept on the extensive royal lands, and others
belonging to the wealthy Benedictine monasteries of Cerne,
Abbotsbury, Milton and Shaftesbury. For example, there were 1,037

sheep on the downs at Cranborne, 1,600 at Puddletown, 900 at Portland and 800 at Burton Bradstock. As well as enriching the arable land, the sheep also provided wool, mutton, milk and cheese.

Occasionally brief glimpses of farming communities can be discerned behind the formal record of the Domesday surveyors. For example Povington on the coast near Tyneham was part of the estates of Robert Fitz Gerald. This included a manorial or demesne farm, that is the land farmed directly by the lord, which was worked by eight serfs and their families. Between them they possessed three ploughs. In addition there were nine smaller farms occupied by villeins. They also shared three ploughs. There was a manorial mill, 8 acres of meadow land, 6 acres of woodland, and pasture 'six furlongs long and as many in width'. Nearly eight centuries later, in 1815 there was still one large farm, surrounded by four smaller farms and eight smallholdings– an increase due to medieval encroachments on the surrounding heath and downland. Here, as in so many parts of Dorset, the farm sites were already in existence long before the coming of the Normans in 1066, and were to survive through all the changes of the later centuries.

ESTATES

The other major characteristic of Dorset which emerges from the Domesday Survey, and was to remain of fundamental importance in the development of farming and rural society in the county, is the preponderance of great estates. In 1086 the Crown was the largest single landowner with a castle at Corfe, widespread manors, and lands which were later to become the royal forests of Blackmore, Gillingham and Powerstock. Another major landowner was the Conqueror's half-brother, Robert, Count of Mortain. Of the extensive lands possessed by the Church, the greatest part belonged to the bishopric of Salisbury, including the castle and extensive lands at Sherborne and the rich estates at Netherbury and Beaminster. Church lands also included the estates of the nunnery at Shaftesbury, the abbeys at Sherborne, Cerne, Milton and Abbotsbury, and numerous smaller religious houses. Glastonbury, Winchester and Wells also possessed lands in the county. Most of the rest of Dorset was in the hands of Norman barons who had dispossessed the former owners.

Much of the evidence for early medieval farming comes from estate records which were carefully kept and preserved by royal officials or the monastic houses. For example, a picture of the farming community at Fontmell near Shaftesbury during the twelfth century emerges from the records of the nunnery at Shaftesbury. In 1135 a survey recorded sixty-five tenants and four mills at Fontmell. Twenty-two of the tenants were villeins holding about 40 acres each, while nineteen others each held about 20 acres. The rest of the community were cottagers with small amounts of land. All the tenants had rights to the extensive sheep pastures on the downland. They grew wheat and barley with occasional crops of rye, beans and peas. Labour services and dues owed by the tenants as rent for their lands are set out in detail. Each villein was obliged to provide either in person or by deputy three days work each week on the nuns' demesne land, and even more at harvest time. They were also required to pay 7d per annum in rent. A generation later, in 1175, another survey reveals that the population had increased. There were now eighty tenants and more land had been brought into cultivation. Many of the labour services had been commuted to money payments, and rents ranged from 2s 6d to 1s 3d per annum, with additional duties such as harvest work on the demesne or carrying produce to the nunnery at Shaftesbury.

A survey of the Dorset estates of Glastonbury abbey at Burton near Sturminster Newton made in 1189 provides a detailed account of farming. The land was cultivated in three large open fields where wheat, barley and oats were grown. Most of the wheat was taken to Glastonbury to feed the numerous monks and the abbey servants. The monastic sheep flocks were carefully managed and were regularly moved long distances between the various manors belonging to the abbey in Somerset and Wiltshire. A 'custumal', or list of manorial regulations and customs, of 1250 sets out the duties required from the tenants by Glastonbury Abbey. For example, one tenant, Robert Tac, who held a tenement of some 40 acres, paid 6s 0d a year in rent and also worked on the demesne for three days each week. In addition, it was stated that 'he ought for the whole year to carry the lord's corn

A surviving medieval landscape on the island of Portland where the strip fields remain unenclosed.

with his beast . . . to Glastonbury or elsewhere at the lord's will'. The tenants' rights are also specified, and amongst other privileges, Robert Tac was to have a dinner provided by the abbot each year on Christmas Day 'to wit bread, cheese, pottage and two dishes of meat'. The tenant was obliged to 'take with him a plate, mug, and a napkin if he wishes to eat off a cloth, and he shall bring a faggot of brushwood to cook his food, unless he would have it raw'.

Evidence of the wealth which came to the monasteries through their farming activities can be seen in the great monastic barns which survive for example, at Abbotsbury, Cerne Abbas, Sydling St Nicholas and Tarrant Crawford. Other fine barns exist at Hinton St Mary and Winterborne Clenston. A late-medieval 'grange' or farmstead together with its barn, formerly part of the Milton abbey estates, remains at Lyscombe in a remote site in Cheselbourne parish.

A notable example of the widespread medieval system whereby farmers held their arable land in scattered strips within large open fields can still be seen on the island of Portland. Strip fields still occupy some 150 acres and provide an admirable indication of the appearance of a medieval landscape.

Strip lynchets at Winspit, showing how medieval cultivation could be extended on to steep hillsides by means of carefully-constructed terraces.

Evidence of the remarkable growth in population, and of the extension of cultivation during the thirteenth century, can be seen in the strip lynchets or terraces by which steep hillsides could be brought under the plough. Whole series of such terraces survive, especially across the chalklands, and there are examples at Maiden Newton, Woolland, Compton Abbas, Bincombe and Worth Matravers, and in west Dorset at Netherbury, Loders and Powerstock.

THE LATER MIDDLE AGES (1300-1500)

The mid-fourteenth century saw the end of the long period of expansion and population growth. A series of wet summers, poor harvests and recurrent visitations of the plague led to a sharp decline in population, the desertion or contraction of some settlements, and the abandonment of marginal land, especially on the chalkland. The Black Death of 1348-49 began in Dorset, spread from a ship berthed at Melcombe Regis, and the county was badly affected by it. During the following decades there were further outbreaks of the plague. In July 1349 the accounts for the royal lands around Bere Regis and

Charminster recorded that there was no income because 'the mortality of men in the present pestilence is so great that the lands thereof be untilled and the profits are lost'.

Over thirty years later Dorset was still being visited by a virulent epidemic, and in 1381 the abbess and nuns of Shaftesbury petitioned for relief from taxation on the grounds that nearly all the tenants on their estates were dead. The results of these disasters are still evident in the numerous deserted sites, such as Stockwood and Stock Gaylard in the Blackmore Vale, Little Piddle and Bardolfston in the Piddle valley, Holworth near Chaldon Herring, Friar Mayne near Broadmayne, and the seven former hamlets in the parish of Charminster. Evidence of contraction can also be seen in former house sites around many villages.

The effect of the economic decline on farming was profound. Much arable land was abandoned and the former ploughlands were converted to grass; many common arable fields with their complex pattern of strips and furlongs were enclosed into separate fields, again for pasture. Above all, the great estates began to concentrate on the increasingly profitable sheep flocks to satisfy the rising demand both at home and abroad for west-country wool and cloth. It was during the fifteenth century that the huge sheep flocks were assembled that were to remain such a distinctive feature of Dorset farming. Some indication of the size of these flocks can be obtained from the details of each of the Dorset monasteries given in the *Valor Ecclesiasticus*, the great survey of Church property taken in 1535 on the eve of the dissolution of the monasteries. The entries for the Dorset monasteries are unique in that they give the number of sheep for each monastery. Between them the Dorset monasteries possessed 24,941 sheep. Milton had over 7,000 sheep, Cerne had more than 6,000, Bindon 3,500, while the nuns at Tarrant Crawford were supported by the income of 3,000 sheep.

Since most medieval records relate to the great estates and their income, it is not easy to find evidence of the life of individual farmers. One exception is a picture of the tenants at Bincombe, on the chalk escarpment overlooking Weymouth, which occurs in a *Inquisition Post Mortem* of 1376. The manor belonged to the small priory of Frampton, and there were 25 villein tenants, each holding eleven acres of arable land plus common grazing rights, and a further seven cottagers holding smaller amounts of land. Their arable lands were in strips divided between the East and West fields, only one of which was cultivated each year. These open fields were to survive until Parliamentary enclosure in 1827. The villeins grew wheat, barley and some oats. They also kept sheep, pigs, cows, oxen to pull the plough, and poultry. The number of livestock, the rights of grazing, the cultivation of the arable lands and all aspects of farming were closely controlled by the detailed list of manorial customs. In return for their land the villeins were obliged to work on the demesne lands for two days a week in winter and for five days a week during the spring sowing and the harvest period. They also paid annual dues of 3d for each cow or ox, 1d for each pig, and a cock and three hens at the feast of St Martin (11 November). The cottagers paid smaller dues, but were obliged to milk the lord's ewes when required, and 'the most honest woman of the whole town (i.e. the community) ought to be dairymaid . . . and make the lord's cheese'. None of the tenants could 'put their sons to learning' nor allow their daughters to marry men from outside the manor without the lord's permission and further payments. They did have some bonuses such as food at harvest time, cheese for each plough they brought to the lord's ploughing, and a dinner at Christmas. Work at threshing for the lord entitled each man to receive eight sheaves 'and the measure of the sheaf is as much as a man can encircle with one arm holding his girdle with his hand'. The annual round of parish feasts and saints' days brought relief and welcome diversions, but for much of the year life for the farmers of Bincombe was a harsh round of heavy labour.

THE SIXTEENTH AND
SEVENTEENTH CENTURIES

This was the period during which the power and influence of a few great landowners became even more dominant in Dorset. The confiscation and rapid sale of the former monastic lands brought about the greatest change in land ownership since the Norman Conquest in 1066. The lands of the Crown, the bishopric of Salisbury, some Oxford and Cambridge colleges and the colleges of Eton and Winchester were already widespread in the county. These institutions, together with some long-established families such as the Clavells, Martyns, Binghams, Turbervilles, Framptons and Russells were now joined by newcomers such as the Cecils, Ashley-Coopers, Tregonwells, Digbys, Arundells, Strangways and Strodes. This period of rapid change offered unprecedented opportunities for the enterprising and ambitious to seize the chance of profit. The local commentator, Thomas Gerard, who lived at Trent near Sherborne, writing during the early seventeenth century, noted the increasing affluence and commented upon the number of families 'who now beginne to encroach upon the Gentrie'. A study of 211 leading Dorset families in 1634 has shown that nearly half appeared in the county for the first time during the previous century.

One effect of the rapid rise of these 'new men' was the construction of grand new manor houses suitable to their enhanced status. Examples include Winterborne Anderson near Bere Regis, built by the Tregonwell family in 1622, Chantmarle near Maiden Newton, built by the Strode family early in the seventeenth century, the Strangways' mansion at Melbury, Sir Walter Raleigh's 'new castle' at Sherborne, and Sir Robert Seymer's house at Hanford near Blandford Forum.

Another effect was that most new estate owners kept meticulous records, so that large numbers of manorial court rolls, surveys, maps, inventories, rentals and accounts survive to give a detailed picture of

Winterborne Anderson Manor was built by the Tregonwell family in 1622, and remains an example of the impact which newly-arrived gentry families had on the landscape.

farming on the estates. Most Dorset farmers were tenants of one of these great estates. They held their land by 'copyhold' tenure for three lives 'according to the custom of the manor'. In general farms remained small, many no more than 20 to 30 acres on the chalk, with extensive common grazing on the downs, and between 30 and 40 acres on the clayland where common grazing was limited.

Sheep were the key to successful arable farming on the Dorset chalklands, and the large flocks of sheep were the feature of Dorset farming which most impressed travellers. John Leland in 1540 wrote that there were 'al about great flokkes of shepe'; and William Camden in 1586 observed that on the chalk downs they 'feed flocks of sheepe in great numbers'. Thomas Gerard in 1620 described the chalk downs as 'all overspread with innumerable Flockes of Sheepe, for which it yields very good and sound Feeding, and from which the Countrie hath reapted an unknowen Gaine'. The impressions of these and other observers are borne out by the evidence of the records.

The flocks kept on the estate or 'demesne' farms were often very large. At East Lulworth in 1515 there were 4,000 sheep on the manor,

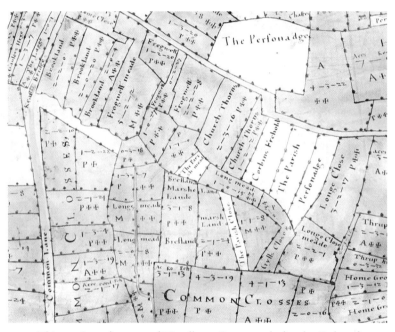

This section of a map of Hazelbury Bryan made for the Duke of Northumberland in 1609 shows the skill of the cartographer Ralph Treswell, and the concern of landowners to have an accurate, detailed record of their land. The symbols denote the size and quality of each field, and a schedule gives the names of the tenants and details of their tenure.

The folding of sheep remained a feature of Dorset chalkland farming until recently, as this photograph of about 1930 shows.

and on the land of Winchester College at Sydling St Nicholas in 1550 there were 2,700 sheep. The Earl of Shaftesbury had 2,750 sheep at Wimborne St Giles in 1670, divided into two flocks, each with its own shepherd. At Puddletown in 1565 there were 3,000 sheep on the demesne farm; at Ashmore in 1590 the demesne flock numbered 1,600, while the manorial tenants kept a further 1,200 sheep. At Winfrith Newburgh in 1598 there were 4,200 sheep on the manor, while Robert Bingham of Melcombe Bingham had a flock of 973 sheep when he died in 1562. Similar examples of large flocks are to be found in estate records and inventories from all over the chalkland.

As well as providing wool, lamb and mutton, the sheep flocks of the chalk downland had another even more important function – enhancing the fertility of the arable land with their dung. Before the advent of artificial fertilisers the fertility of the thin chalkland soils could only be maintained by the intensive folding of flocks of sheep, which fed all day on the downlands and were close-folded at night on the arable land on the lower slopes. The sheep were an essential factor in the successful production of wheat and barley, the main cash crops for chalkland farmers. For an efficient sheep-fold it was necessary to have a large number of sheep, so that on most chalkland manors the sheep of all the tenants were kept in a single common flock with a shepherd who was employed by the whole manor. The shepherd had to supervise the sheep on the downland each day, and each evening pen them in a fold on the arable land, moving the fold daily so as to cover each tenant's land in turn. The necessity for a common sheep flock to manure the ground was one of the main reasons why communal organisation of agriculture and the arrangement of each tenant's land in scattered strips within large open fields survived longest on the chalklands. The type of sheep kept was the old Dorset breed, the forerunner of the breed which later became famous as the Dorset Horn. They were hardy, large-limbed animals, capable of walking long distances over the downs. They had white legs and faces, and both sexes had curled horns. The characteristic which most distinguished them was the readiness of the ewes to produce early lambs from late autumn onwards. They were a docile breed, admirably suited to folding on bare fallows and newly-ploughed land destined for corn crops.

The sheep-fold continued until the later nineteenth century to be the mainstay of Dorset chalkland farming. Most chalkland settlements remained strung out along the river valleys, with few farms on the higher downland. The arable land occupied the lower slopes, and the survival of the open fields where farming was closely regulated by long-established customs meant that manorial organisation remained strong.

THE HEATH AND THE CLAY VALES

The acid, ill-drained soils of the heath which occupied much of south-east Dorset remained in much the same state as when John Leland saw it in 1540 and wrote of the 'low, blak, morish ground, over growen with heth and mosse'. Around the edge of the heath and in parts of Purbeck there was some arable, growing oats, barley and rye, but elsewhere farmers concentrated on dairy farming and the raising of cattle, pigs, horses and ponies.

In the clay vales of north and west Dorset the main object of farming was the breeding of cattle and the production of butter and cheese. Sheep were also raised for sale to chalkland farmers whose folding flocks needed constant replacements. Farms remained small and scattered and there were few common arable fields.

One of the best sources of evidence about farming comes from the probate inventories which were required before a will could be proved. They reveal that many clayland farmers had no arable land at all. William Deane of Castleton near Sherborne, who died in 1604, had no crops listed in his inventory, but possessed six cows, four steers and thirteen pigs. In his milkhouse and dairy he had numerous pewter vessels and cheese vats; he also had four stones (56lbs) of cheese and a large quantity of butter. Richard Brydle, who died in 1639, farmed on the heavy clay at Holnest. He was unusually wealthy and kept 15 cows and a bull, 11 steers, 6 calves and 3 pigs. He also had a quantity of milk pans and 10 cwt. of cheese.

A remarkable feature of Dorset dairy farming was the practice of farmers renting out their cows to a dairyman by the year. The farmer provided the cows together with their pasture, and a house and dairy. This explains the numerous farms with separate dairy establishments or 'dairy houses' throughout Dorset. The dairyman undertook the labour-intensive, specialist work of producing and marketing the butter and cheese. This system was to continue until the nineteenth century and is described by Thomas Hardy in *Tess of the d'Urbervilles*. Many agreements for renting dairies occur in estate records. For example, in 1648 Nicholas Hardy of Beaminster agreed to rent 20 cows from Sir John Strode of Parnham; the cows to be pastured in Parnham Park for £2 14s 0d each per annum and winter fodder was to be provided for them. In 1697 John Hansford rented a house, dairy and eight cows from John Gibbs of Edmondsham for £2 6s 8d per annum for each cow, with pasture and fodder provided. The importance of butter and cheese in the farming economy of the claylands is shown by the prominent place these products occupied in local markets and fairs. Thomas Gerard in 1620 wrote of Yeovil market that 'its greatest commodity is cheese which being made in greate abundance in the adjoyninge country is weekly transported hence both into Wilts and Hampshire in very great quantity'. Cheese, butter, hides, leather and tallow were likewise important in the markets at Bridport, Dorchester, Sherborne and Shaftesbury, and in the numerous smaller markets such as Cerne Abbas, Cranborne and Evershot, where today only traces of the former market places survive as reminders of their past importance.

Large quantities of these products from the dairy farms of the clay

The scene at a Dorset sheep fair. Such fairs were an essential feature of the farming economy from the Middle Ages, selling all kinds of produce as well as livestock.

vales were also sold in the important hill-top fairs held annually at Whitedown near Chard and on Woodbury Hill near Bere Regis. Much butter and cheese was also transported out of the county by carriers' carts. Legal disputes provide evidence of sheep and cattle sales, and of the annual influx of cattle from Wales which were fattened in Dorset before being driven on to London or Portsmouth. The accounts of stock kept on the Earl of Shaftesbury's estate at Wimborne St Giles show that cattle for fattening were regularly purchased from drovers. When the royal forest of Gillingham was enclosed during the 1620s and some of the roads through the forest were blocked, there were protests from Welsh cattle drovers who had traditionally used the roads for their livestock. Of course most livestock sales were conducted without any formal record being made. Nicholas Fill and Robert Gawpin were cattle dealers from Lydlinch in the Blackmore Vale during the 1630s and regularly drove cattle to London for sale. In 1634 they agreed to buy forty steers from three Cornishmen whom they met in London. The cattle were to be delivered at Exeter on a specified day, and after fattening in Dorset were to be driven to Smithfield market in London. No doubt such arrangements were common. A record of this agreement only survives because of a subsequent dispute between the parties over the price of the cattle. The diary of John Richards of Warmwell records that in May 1694 he travelled to Glamorgan to buy cattle, crossing from Bridgwater and going to Bridgend Fair. He bought 42 head of cattle and brought them back to Warmwell.

Many sheep bred in Somerset and west Dorset were sold to farmers on the chalkland for replenishing their folding flocks. Records of some of these transactions survive because buyers often demanded a warranty that the sheep were free from disease. For example, William Downe of Charlton Horethorne sold 26 sheep to John Oke at Sherborne in May 1649 for £12 15s 0d, and warranted them free from disease. Subsequently most of the sheep died, and Oke unsuccessfully claimed £30 in compensation. John Adams, who farmed on the chalkland at Piddlehinton, insisted on a warranty with the sheep he purchased from the low-lying land at Misterton near Crewkerne in 1688, and later claimed to be refunded when the sheep proved to be infected with liver fluke.

The Dorset Horn sheep is renowned for its ability to produce lambs very early in the year, and there was a considerable trade in spring lambs for the London market. Early in the eighteenth century Daniel Defoe commented on the importance of the trade, and the accounts of the Strode family of Chantmarle record sales of lambs and in-lamb ewes to dealers in Kent, Sussex, Surrey and Hertfordshire, as well as to the London market.

ENCLOSURES AND INNOVATIONS

The 'new men' who rose to prominence in the economic and religious upheavals of the sixteenth century were keen to exploit the resources of their estates in every possible way. One profitable method was through enclosure; another was greatly to increase the size of the demesne sheep flocks. There are numerous examples of the eviction of tenants to create sheep-grazing land, to accommodate a larger

The village of Stour Provost from a large early-eighteenth century map at King's College, Cambridge, showing some of the enclosures which the tenants were persuaded to make during the 1620s.

demesne flock or to enclose land which had formerly been common. At Iwerne Courtney (Shroton) near Blandford Forum a survey in 1548 recorded that 'The customary (i.e. copyhold) tenants were so smale and so little lande longing to them that they were not able to pay the lord's rent, but one half of them departed the towne . . .'. The lands were then enclosed and allocated among the remaining tenants. By 1553 only four tenants remained on the manor, but the records are silent about the fate of those who had 'departed the towne'.

In 1604 Sir Anthony Ashley of Wimborne St Giles forced his tenants to agree to a division of the sheep downs by threatening that he would increase the size of his own sheep flock and extend his rabbit warren if they refused. It is no accident that Wimborne St Giles is surrounded by numerous deserted or derelict settlements. Along the Winterborne valley south of Dorchester a string of deserted villages shows where the tenants waged an unsuccessful campaign against being over-run by the sheep flocks of their landlord. At Winterborne Faringdon where today only the ruins of the church survive, the tenants had already been driven out by the 1620s, and Thomas Gerard described 'a lone church, for there is hardlie any house left in the parish, such of late hath been the Covetousness of some private Men, that to increase their demesnes have depopulated whole parishes'.

At Stour Provost in 1620 great pressure was put upon the tenants by the landlord, Kings College, Cambridge, to agree to enclosure and re-allocation of the arable land. Many tenants objected but were finally forced to agree 'albeit after much solicitation and entreaty'. The result can still be seen in the landscape, since the hedges around the new fields follow the curving lines of the former strip system. Not all encroachments on tenants' rights by wealthy men were successful. In 1624 John Warham, gentleman, enclosed the village green at Osmington, which the villagers had traditionally used for recreation and playing bowls. Evidence given to the Court of Star Chamber reveals that a large crowd assembled at night with weapons and tore down the hedges which Warham had erected, 'and used John Warham's own wood to erect a gallows on his land where they hung his effigy, amid great rejoicings'.

Another feature of Dorset agriculture during this period was the introduction of new and profitable crops. Among these were clover, rye-grass and sainfoin, all of which were grown for cattle fodder. Cabbages as a field crop grown for cattle were said to have been first grown in England by Sir Anthony Ashley of Wimborne St Giles, who introduced them from Holland. On the rich soils of west Dorset flax was grown by some farmers and used for the manufacture of linen, canvas and sailcloth. Flax was a labour-intensive crop and was generally grown in small plots. Numerous fields in west Dorset still bear the name Flaxlands or Flax Close.

The growing of woad was also introduced during the later sixteenth century. Woad, which produced a soft blue dye, and was the basis of all the dark colours used in the woollen cloth industry, had previously been imported. Woad was a hungry crop, and was seldom grown for long in the same place. It was potentially very profitable and was soon widely grown in west Dorset. It was also grown around Cranborne where it supplied dye to the clothiers of Salisbury. When the former deer park belonging to Sir Robert Cecil at Blagdon near Cranborne was leased out to tenants for agricultural use early in the seventeenth century, many of those who rented parts of the land used it to grow woad. Among them was the Salisbury lawyer Henry Sherfield, who acted as steward for the Earl of Salisbury's west-country estates. Sherfield's account book shows that he continued until his death in 1634 to grow large quantities of woad. One of the pages of his accounts still has attached to it a small sample of woollen cloth dyed with his woad. This retains the attractive deep blue colour characteristic of the dye from this plant.

Another crop which had previously been imported was hemp, which was introduced during the sixteenth century and soon became an important feature of the farming economy in west Dorset, the area around Corfe Castle, and some parts of the Stour valley. Hemp was used in the manufacture of rope and twine at Bridport, Beaminster, Crewkerne and elsewhere. Like flax and woad, hemp is a labour-intensive, hungry crop and grew well on the rich soil of west Dorset. Thomas Fuller, vicar of Broadwindsor from 1634 to 1641, wrote in his book, *The Worthies of England,* that 'England hath no better [hemp] than what groweth here betixt Beaminster and Bridport'.

The cultivation of these new and profitable crops was greatly encouraged by the gentry of the county, eager to enhance the return from their land. A group of gentlemen headed by Sir Thomas Freke of Iwerne Courtney set up demonstration plots for the cultivation and processing of flax and hemp during the 1620s, and persuaded their tenants to grow these crops. The account book of Sir John Strode of Parnham near Beaminster covering the years 1648-68 shows him exploiting all the resources of his estates. He cultivated hemp himself, and rented out small hemp plots to his tenants, charging a much higher rent than for ordinary agricultural land.

Hops were also being grown in the county by the 1630s. In a case before the court of Chancery in 1634 William Samways, a carrier from Preston near Weymouth, gave evidence of having taken a bag of hops 'as much as three men could lifte upon the shambles of a carte', from Durweston to Salisbury for transport to London. In a case over the sale of hops at Yeovil market in 1653 the defendant claimed to have had 158 lbs. of locally-grown hops for sale, and stated that he regularly sold hops in the market.

In their eagerness to increase the returns from their estates, it was the landowners who encouraged and pressed for other changes in

Farming operations from corn harvest and threshing
to milking portrayed in a medieval manuscript illustration.

traditional farming practices. An example is Theophilus, Earl of Suffolk, whose widespread Dorset estates were centred on Lulworth Castle. He was actively engaged in improvements to his property with increased sheep flocks, enclosures and drainage schemes. In 1636 he entered into an agreement with his tenants at Lodmoor near Weymouth whereby a low-lying strip of marshy ground was drained, adding to the productive land and increasing his rent income.

Drainage and land reclamation was also undertaken on Brownsea Island, around the shores of Poole Harbour and in many parts of the heath and the clay vales. Not all were successful, and the most ambitious scheme proved to be a total and expensive disaster. This was a plan produced during the 1630s by a number of landowners headed by Sir George Horsey of Clifton Maybank near Sherborne to drain the Fleet, the large area of tidal water lying between the Chesil Beach and the mainland. More than £1,000 was spent on the project, but in spite of some initial success high tides and winter storms soon engulfed the reclaimed land. The failure brought about the final ruin of the Horsey family and the dispersal of their estates. Sir George was imprisoned for debt in Dorchester gaol and died there.

WATER MEADOWS

By far the most important innovation of the seventeenth century, and Dorset's major contribution to agricultural progress, was the introduction and rapid spread of artificially-watered meadows. Using an elaborate system of hatches, channels and drains, meadow land lying beside a fast-flowing chalkland stream could be covered by a thin sheet of moving water, protecting the grass from frost and encouraging a much more rapid growth during the spring than would have occurred naturally. The first fully-developed systems of water meadows were introduced along the chalk streams of Dorset and south Wiltshire during the early seventeenth century, and thereafter spread into other parts of the country. By creating a means of producing early grass, the water meadows enabled chalkland farmers to overcome the age-old problem of providing sufficient feed for livestock during the early spring. During the summer water meadows also provided abundant crops of hay. They enabled farmers to keep larger flocks of sheep for folding on the arable land, and thus to produce heavier crops of wheat and barley. Until the late nineteenth century they were to remain a crucial feature of the sheep-corn husbandry of the Dorset chalkland.

The construction of a water meadow was a complex and expensive undertaking, generally carried out as a communal project, and manorial records show the way in which landlords encouraged their tenants to adopt such profitable improvements. It was the active support of the Earl of Pembroke which led to the construction of so many water meadows in south Wiltshire, and it was landowners such as the Earl of Suffolk, and the Hastings, Lawrence, Weld, Trenchard, Strangways and Ashley-Cooper families who urged the adoption of numerous schemes along the chalk streams of Dorset. The first evidence for a fully-developed water meadow anywhere in the country occurs in the manorial records of Affpuddle in 1605-10. The landlord,

Henry Hastings, whose estate included
Mappowder, Woodland and Puddletown – where
he played an active part in the creation of
one of the earliest water meadows.
The illustration shows him at the age of
87 in 1638. He died in 1650 aged 99.

Edward Lawrence, was interested in agricultural improvements and
encouraged the tenants to dig the necessary channels and drains,
install hatches in the river and construct ridges along which the water
could flow and spread out over the surface of the meadow. In 1610
three men were appointed to supervise the watering of the meadow,
and the tenants agreed to share the costs. Evidently the scheme was a
success, and by 1629 it had been copied by the farmers at Puddletown
'for the watering and Improvinge of their groundes in Broadmoor'. At
the manorial court held at Puddletown in October 1629 the landlord,
Henry Hastings, was present when 'a greate debate beinge theare had
and questions moved by some of the tenants', it was agreed that one
of the leaseholders, Richard Russell, and others, should be allowed to
continue with the work already started for creating a water meadow.
In this new and untried project, success was not assured, and the
agreement contained a provision that the tenants should restore the
meadow if the scheme did not lead to a great improvement. They were

evidently prepared to accept the risk of failure in their enthusiasm to press ahead with the enterprise. During the 1630s there are references to water meadows being constructed at several places along the Frome and Piddle valleys. For example at Winfrith Newburgh in 1636 the Earl of Suffolk agreed to share the costs of a water meadow with his tenants, 'in consideration the said Earle is pleased by way of watering . . . to improve the meadow called Winfrith Mead'. The agreement was signed by the Earl and twenty-two tenants. In his *Survey of Dorset* written during the 1630s, the local landowner, Thomas Gerard, described the river Frome passing 'amongst most pleasant Meadows, manie of which of late yeares have been by Industrie soe made of barren Bogges'. By the later seventeenth century water meadows were to be found along all the chalk valleys of Dorset, and had spread into some clayland areas.

CONSTRUCTION AND OPERATION

The work of laying out a water meadow with precise levels, a ridged, free-draining surface, and the essential hatches, channels and drains, required a great deal of work and careful surveying. It required considerable expertise to divert a fast-flowing stream by hatches and to ensure that the meadow was covered with a thin sheet of moving water. It was essential that the water was kept moving, otherwise it would kill the grass rather than encourage its growth. 'On at a trot and off at a gallop' was the ideal for the water. When a water meadow was constructed beside the Stour at Charlton Marshall in 1659 'able and sufficient carpenters' were obtained from Tolpuddle for building the hatches in the river, and Henry Phelps of Turners Puddle, 'a known Ancient, Able and Experienced waterman', was sent for to supervise the whole project. The scheme was encouraged by the landowners, Sir Ralph Bankes and the Provost of Eton College. Thirty-six tenants also contributed to the work which cost £62 12s 6d.

Once established, the operation of the water meadows was controlled by a 'waterman', who imposed a strictly regulated calendar. By the end of September each year the hatches, channels and drains would have been checked and cleared. Watering could then begin for short periods, depending on the weather. The aim was to protect the

The complex system of hatches and channels for water meadows in the River Frome at Stinsford.

grass from frost, to allow winter floods to deposit valuable nutrients around the roots and to encourage an early growth. Coming from underground reservoirs in the chalk, the water of the chalk streams was at a constant temperature and therefore ideal for protecting the grass. A lush growth of grass could be produced by late March, and this was used to feed the ewes and lambs which were allowed to graze for short periods each day. Straight from the fresh grass they were folded upon the land destined for spring-sown barley. This was the period when the water meadows really paid for the costs of construction and operation. The sheep did not feed in the meadows after the beginning of May, since then they were liable to contract liver-fluke and foot-rot from the damp pasture. The meadows could then be watered for a few days and then left for a hay crop. Watered meadows would produce a heavy crop, even if there was a summer drought. During late summer cattle or milking cows were allowed to graze in the meadows, before the annual round began once more.

GEORGE BOSWELL (1735-1815)

One of the first practical accounts of the construction and operation of water meadows was written by a Dorset farmer, George Boswell, who lived at Puddletown and later rented Waddock Farm, Affpuddle, from the landowner, James Frampton of Moreton. Boswell was deeply interested in new farming methods and new machinery. He built himself a seed drill and a threshing machine, and made numerous experiments, describing his work in the influential *Journal* of the Bath and West Agricultural Society, which was founded in 1777. His national reputation was established in 1779 with the publication of his book *A Treatise on Watering Meadows*. This provided details of the benefits of water meadows, instructions on their operation, and diagrams of hatches, channels, tools and techniques. It was essentially a practical guide, based on Boswell's own experience, and the book achieved considerable success. A second, larger edition was published in 1790.

As a result of his book, farmers from many parts of the country visited Boswell, including a leading farmer from Northumberland, George Culley. Letters from Boswell to Culley covering the years 1787-1805 give much detail concerning Dorset farming, especially about sheep and water meadows. Culley also sent one of his workmen to Dorset so that he could learn about water meadows from Boswell. The workman, Harry, stayed with Boswell for seven months before returning to Northumberland to introduce the techniques he had learnt in Dorset.

THE DECLINE OF THE MEADOWS

For two centuries water meadows were an essential feature of farming throughout the Dorset chalk region, but during the later nineteenth century the water meadows began to fall into disuse. The introduction of artificial fertilisers meant that the folding of the sheep flock was no longer necessary for growing satisfactory crops of corn on the downland. New fodder crops and new strains of cultivated grass and clover could be substituted for water-meadow grass. The water meadows were labour-intensive and expensive to maintain, and they could not easily be worked with modern machinery. Above all, the prolonged agricultural depression from the 1880s brought profound changes to Dorset farming, in particular the abandonment of sheep/corn husbandry. Today the chalkland valleys have many hundreds of acres of former water meadows, easily recognisable with their hatches and channels, but mostly presenting a sorry picture of neglect and decay.

In only a few places have they survived. Examples of meadows still being watered can be seen at Wolfeton on the Frome, north of Dorchester and on the Dewlish Brook, east of Puddletown. Some Wiltshire water meadows continue to be managed in the traditional way along the Avon south of Salisbury, notably at Britford.

LANDLORDS, TENANT FARMERS AND LANDLESS LABOURERS 1715-1815

This period witnessed population increase, the spectacular growth of industrial towns, and culminated in the upheavals of the Napoleonic Wars; it also brought hitherto undreamt of prices for farm produce and saw profound changes in Dorset farming. The pressure for higher yields led to numerous 'improvements', including a great increase in enclosures, more downland and pasture converted to arable, the amalgamation of farms, new farm buildings and the emergence of a large class of landless labourers entirely dependent upon wages to support themselves and their families. The contrast between the fine houses and opulent lifestyle of the land-owning gentry and the comfortable existence of the wealthier tenant farmers on the one hand, and the poverty, bad housing and long hours of work of the labourers was to remain characteristic of Dorset until the later nineteenth century.

The contrasting geology of Dorset continued to condition the farming and landscape of the different regions. When the author and journalist Daniel Defoe journeyed through the county in 1720 he described the heathland around Wimborne as 'a sandy, wild and barren country'. Describing the heath in 1771, Arthur Young wrote of 'vast tracts of waste land that cry aloud for improvements', adding, with supreme disregard for the practical difficulties, 'What fortunes are here to be made by spirited improvers!'. In the chalkland region Defoe was impressed by 'the vast flocks of sheep' and by the downland grass where centuries of close-grazing by the sheep had produced 'all fine carpet ground, soft as velvet, and the herbage sweet as garden herbs'. It was the huge sheep flocks which continued to be the aspect of Dorset farming which most impressed observers. In his

Dorset Horn sheep from a print published in 1841.

Report for the newly-formed Board of Agriculture in 1793, John Claridge wrote enthusiastically that, 'The most striking feature of the county is the open and uninclosed parts, covered by numerous flocks of sheep, scattered over the Downs'. In 1796 the agricultural writer William Marshall described the rich soils of west Dorset, around Bridport, Beaminster and the Marshwood Vale, which produced heavy crops of wheat, beans, flax and hemp. He also commented on the scattered farmsteads, and especially the dairy farms, the small irregular fields with thick hedgerows and the widespread production of butter and cheese for the London market.

INNOVATION AND IMPROVEMENT

During the eighteenth century the great estates increasingly persuaded or coerced their tenant farmers into exchanging the ancient copyhold tenure for fixed-term leases. This was a change which gave landlords much greater control of the land, with a regular economic rental income in place of the old, uncertain system of low rents and heavy entry fines when a tenant died and a new name was inserted into the copyhold. Unlike copyhold tenure, leases were not subject to the customs of the manor, and landlords could insist that tenants adopted the best farming techniques and modern methods. They could also amalgamate holdings and install tenants with the necessary capital and ambition to introduce modern methods of farming and crop rotation.

Among the Dorset landowners most enthusiastic for progressive farming was Humphrey Sturt of Crichel. As well as rebuilding his mansion and re-locating the village of More Crichel, he revolutionised the farming on his estate, introducing new crops, undertaking land reclamation and drainage, promoting enclosures and bringing ashes and fertilisers by barge from London to enrich the land for his plantations on Brownsea Island. Other notable improvers were the Framptons of Moreton, the Damers of Came and the Welds of Lulworth. Joseph Damer, Lord Dorchester of Milton Abbey, is best remembered for having demolished the town of Milton Abbas to create the park around his mansion, but he was also a leading exponent of modern farming methods – as Arthur Young noted: 'The public is not a little indebted to this nobleman for attending with so much propriety to the improvement of the husbandry of Dorset'. Landowners also devoted much energy to the improvement of their estates by the planting of trees, and the results of their work can still be seen in many parts of the county. During the Napoleonic Wars the Frampton family of Moreton planted many thousands of trees on their estate, completely changing the appearance of that part of Dorset. At the same time Scots Pine began to be planted on parts of the heath, creating a remarkable transformation in the previously bleak landscape.

New farming societies helped to spread information about the latest methods and about new breeds of livestock. The earliest and most important was the Bath and West of England Agricultural Society which was founded in 1777; it influenced farmers through its shows, meetings, lectures, exhibitions, practical demonstrations and publications. The high prices and optimism of the later eighteenth century are reflected in the solidly-built farmhouses, barns and dairies. New farms were established on the newly-enclosed downland, some of which can still be recognised by their names, for example Botany Bay, Normandy, Canada, Quatre Bras, or simply New Farm.

In the dairy farming regions of north and west Dorset, improvements to the road system with the introduction of turnpike roads made the rapid dispatch and sale of cheese and butter much easier. By the late eighteenth century waggons carrying butter and cheese from Dorset could reach London in four days. Dorset butter enjoyed a high reputation and commanded a premium in the London market. Prices rose from 6d per pound in 1750 to 1s 2d per pound in 1800 when war conditions had inflated all food prices. Most of the cheese sent out of the county was hard Cheddar-type, made in 100 lb truckles. The softer Blue Vinney cheese did not travel well. Dorset dairy farms also benefited from the market for milk, butter, cheese and other dairy-farm products such as eggs, pork and bacon, created by the growing resorts of Weymouth and Lyme Regis.

Although it was strongly criticised by observers such as William Marshall and Arthur Young, the Dorset system of rented dairies continued. It gave little incentive for improvement in methods or in livestock breeding, but it did provide an opportunity for ambitious and hard-working labourers to achieve a measure of independence. Most dairy farms in north and west Dorset remained as small family-run enterprises, although a few became much larger. For example, in 1807 when food prices and optimism were at their height, William Mayo, gentleman, of Friar Whaddon in Portesham parish, agreed to rent a dairy to Richard Boyland, dairyman. Boyland was to have a dairy-house, milk-house and stable together with 'forty-five good milch cows and pasture for them', in return for the very high rent of £10 per annum for each cow. Mayo was to provide 'sufficient herbage, pasture and provender according to the rules of Dairies used and approved in the neighbourhood'. This was an exceptionally large dairy herd, although Thomas Hardy depicts a similar dairy employing numerous milk-maids in *Tess of the d'Urbervilles*. A rented dairy of 15-25 cows was more typical.

Many farmers throughout the claylands and Cranborne Chase profited from woodland crafts such as the manufacture of hurdles, rakes, gates, posts, thatching spars and the sale of underwood, activities described so well by Thomas Hardy in *The Woodlanders*.

ENCLOSURE AND THE INCREASING
SIZE OF FARMS

The innovations introduced during the eighteenth century required capital, and this encouraged the amalgamation of farms, the enclosure of open arable fields with their inconvenient scattering of strips, and the requirement for each farmer to grow the same crops and adhere to the same timetable. Such changes undoubtedly brought greater efficiency, increased productivity and higher rents for landlords, but meant that many small farms disappeared and their tenants were compelled to join the growing ranks of landless labourers. The small farmers on the downland were doomed to failure. Small farms were progressively squeezed out by economic circumstances, changed conditions, the costs of enclosure, and above all, by the greater efficiency of large-scale farming on the chalk downs. Landlords favoured large and highly profitable farms, and often refused to renew copyhold tenures, adding the small tenements to the larger farms.

Many earlier enclosures had been carried out by agreement between landlords and tenants and without the expense of obtaining an Act of Parliament. For example, in 1695 the arable fields of East and West Morden, on the edge of the heathland, were enclosed by agreement between Thomas Erle of Charborough and his tenants. The

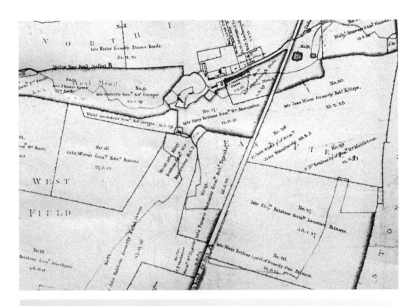

Opposite page & above. Three illustrations of Winterborne Monkton, which belonged to the Dean & Chapter of Exeter cathedral.
Opposite page. Map of 1774 showing the village houses along the stream with three large open fields and surrounding downland. Note the straight Roman road running south from Dorchester.
Above. Enclosure map of 1816 showing a complete transformation of the landscape, with the Roman road as almost the only surviving feature. This was soon followed by an amalgamation of holdings and the disappearance of several smaller farms.
The photograph shows the same landscape today.

agreement recognised that 'great part of the Lands within the said manor Ly dispersed in Common Fields to the hindrance and obstruction of Improvement and Good Husbandry which might be made thereon if the same were separate and enclosed as well to the Profitt and advantage of the owners and occupyers thereof'. Thomas Erle encouraged the tenants to exchange their strips and enclose the land by providing wood for fencing and undertaking not to raise the rents during the lifetime of existing tenants. To supervise the allotment of the land to each tenant three arbitrators were appointed, two from Bere Regis and one from Bloxworth. The common grazing land of the manor was not included, and remained open until a Parliamentary enclosure in 1869.

It was the loss of common grazing rights which most severely hit the smaller tenants. At Winfrith Newburgh in 1768 nearly 3,000 acres of arable, meadow, downland and heath were enclosed. The landlord, Edward Weld, was allocated 1,144 acres, ten larger farmers shared another 1,495 acres, leaving less than 400 acres to be divided among 50 smaller tenants. During the next few years most of the small-holders sold their small plots to the larger farmers. In 1797 a visitor to Durweston reported that there had been nearly 30 small farms before enclosure, but that now two large farms occupied almost all the land in the parish.

The fate of the small farmers of Bere Regis was typical of many hundreds of others right across the chalklands and around the edges of the heath. In 1776 there were 46 tenant farmers with 2,037 acres, of whom 26 had less than thirty acres each. During the next twenty years the smaller tenements were amalgamated to form larger holdings, the inconveniently-scattered strips in the common arable fields were thrown together and enclosed by the more enterprising tenants, and by 1796 the 26 smaller holdings had been swallowed up by the larger farms, even though formal Parliamentary enclosure did not occur until 1846. In the dairy-farming parish of Trent, the number of farms declined from 68 in 1740 to 41 in 1783 and by 1839 the number had sunk to 12.

The rising prices obtained for farm produce provided an irresistible motive for enclosure. This was especially true during the Napoleonic War. Between 1793 and 1815 the price of beef, mutton and barley doubled, and the price of wheat increased threefold. Although the process of Parliamentary enclosure was generally fair, the costs and restrictions, together with the loss of common grazing land, meant that many small-holders were forced to abandon the land. By 1815 many of the open arable fields with their complex arrangement of strips and furlongs, had been enclosed, creating the present landscape of rectangular fields and hedgrows.

Not all proposals for enclosure were successful. An attempt by the larger landowners to secure the enclosure of the lands belonging to the large manor of Fordington failed because of the concerted opposition from the many small-holders. Enclosure was therefore postponed until 1876. On the island of Portland a majority of the many tenants of this royal manor refused to agree to any change, and the open fields continue to exist.

For most Dorset farm labourers, conditions deteriorated greatly during the eighteenth century, until by the end of the century the county had become notorious for the low wages, long hours and poor housing of its workers. All over the county, parish Poor Law account books show increasing demands for relief and rapidly rising poor rates as wages failed to keep pace with the increasing price of food. When Sir Frederick Morton Eden visited Dorset in 1790 to collect material for his great survey of *The State of the Poor* (published 1797) he found a shocking state of affairs. Around Blandford Forum he reported that farm labourers received no more than 6s od or 7s od per week, and many families received regular poor relief. He commented that the destitution was 'generally attributed to the high price of provisions, the smallness of wages, and the consolidation of small farms, and the consequent depopulation of villages, which obliges small farmers to turn labourers or servants . . .'. Conditions for Dorset labourers and their families were to get even worse during the next century.

'HIGH FARMING' DURING THE NINETEENTH CENTURY

The immediate effect of the ending of the long war against Napoleon with the victory at Waterloo in 1815, was a period of depression, with rapidly falling prices for farm produce. The prices which farmers could obtain for wheat, barley, beef, mutton and cheese, all fell by 50 per cent or more between 1815 and 1820. Those who had borrowed money to support improvements such as enclosures or new buildings, found themselves in difficulties, and there were numerous bankruptcies. During the same period the condition of the poorly-paid and badly-housed labourers and their families became even worse. During the war wages had increased, though not enough to compensate for the rapid rise in the price of food, but after the war wages fell to 6s od per week in winter and 7s od in summer. Unemployment and poverty increased rapidly, and many more families were forced to seek poor relief. Many would have wholeheartedly agreed with William Cobbett's protest at the condition of the labourers in south Wiltshire: 'This is I verily believe it, the worst used labouring people upon the face of the earth. Dogs and hogs and horses are treated with more civility; and as to food and lodging, how gladly would the labourers change with them!'.

It was the combination of low wages, poor conditions and unemployment that led to a great explosion of anger by the labourers across southern England in November 1830. The labourers' revolt was known as the Swing Riots, called after Captain Swing, the fictitious leader of the rioters. In Dorset the riots, which involved rick burning, machine breaking and threats to prominent farmers and landowners, were concentrated in the corn-growing chalklands between Wimborne and Dorchester, and in the traditionally lawless region of Cranborne Chase. Both areas had vast estates and large

A view of Abbotsbury. This idealised picture of the countryside was far from the reality of life for most Dorset labourers and their families.

farms where the hated threshing machines which deprived labourers of a major part of their traditional work had been introduced.

There were more than forty riots in Dorset, including major gatherings of belligerent labourers around Wareham, Sixpenny Handley, Blandford, Puddletown and Shaftesbury, demanding that wages be increased to 10s od per week. The riots were ruthlessly suppressed, the ring-leaders were arrested and sixty-two prisoners were tried at Dorchester in January 1831, of whom fifteen were jailed and thirteen were sentenced to transportation. Wages and conditions remained much as before. Another attempt by a few labourers to improve their conditions was made at Tolpuddle in 1833-4. About forty labourers joined a Friendly Society or Trade Union to press for higher wages. They fell foul of the harsh laws against assemblies and trade unions, and with the memory of the Swing Riots still fresh in their minds, the magistrates, led by James Frampton of Moreton, acted swiftly. Six of the ringleaders were arrested, and after a trial at

Dorchester were sentenced to transportation. Their fate aroused great national indignation; they became known as the Tolpuddle Martyrs, and after a campaign of public protest the six men were pardoned and brought back to England.

HIGH FARMING

The farming depression which followed the end of the war in 1815 abated during the 1820s, and for the next five decades Dorset farming enjoyed a golden period of Victorian prosperity. In spite of fears that the Repeal of the Corn Laws in 1846 would lead to an influx of foreign corn, this failed to materialise, and farmers could concentrate on introducing the many new ideas, techniques, new breeds of livestock, new fodder crops, labour-saving machines and steam engines which now became readily available. These improvements were summed up in the contemporary term 'high farming', which meant high capital investment in buildings, livestock, implements, artificial fertilisers and drainage, producing in return high yields of corn, milk and fodder crops. For landowners, the high yields could be reflected in higher rents, and this period was also a golden age for the great estates which dominated Dorset.

'High Farming' also meant the pursuit of excellence in all branches of agriculture, and the application of scientific methods and modern techniques. Writing in 1854 Louis H. Ruegg, who was the editor of a Dorset newspaper and a perceptive observer of its agriculture, wrote that 'From Woodyates (in the N.E. corner of Dorset) to six miles beyond Dorchester (nearly the entire length of the chalk district) there is no better farming in the Kingdom'.

The massive expansion in the population of the industrial towns created a ready market for farm produce, and the coming of the railways to Dorset provided a rapid means of transport to all parts of the country. The railways reached Dorchester by 1847, Yetminster, Evershot, Maiden Newton, Bridport and Weymouth by 1857, Gillingham, Blandford and Sherborne by 1860 and Sturminster Newton by 1862. Few places were unaffected by the new facilities. The railways brought artificial fertilisers, machinery, new building materials, drainage pipes and oil cake for cattle, sheep and horses. The

The Wessex Saddleback breed was an ideal 'dairyman's pig' which was developed during the nineteenth century and soon became popular.

new transport revolutionised Dorset dairy farming, since for the first time liquid milk could be carried rapidly to the towns.

The mid-nineteenth century also saw a new scientific approach to farming. The new ideas were spread by farmers' clubs which were established throughout Dorset. They provided lectures, exhibitions and competitions, while the *Journal* of the Bath and West Society, together with the annual shows and demonstrations, continued to publicise the best and most modern practice.

Conscious of the higher rents which could be charged for their farms, many landowners encouraged the adoption of new methods, partly by example and partly by laying down strict conditions in the leases they granted, specifying crop rotations, livestock management and modern husbandry. On the Digby estates around Sherborne farmers were presented with no less than twenty-three clauses in their leases. At Bryanston, Lord Portman demonstrated the new ideas on his own farms, as did John James Farquharson at Langton Long, Henry Charles Sturt at More Crichel and Lord Rivers on his large estate on Cranborne Chase. Landowners also instigated large-scale drainage schemes, using the newly-available clay pipes. On the wide-ranging estates of the Earl of Shaftesbury several thousand pounds were spent each year on drainage work, and similar work was carried out on the Digby, Strangways and Russell estates. During the 1840s and 1850s

Hoeing at New Barn Farm, Abbotsbury in 1900. Mechanisation and the elimination of the need for a large labour force have transformed twentieth-century farming. It would be inconceivable to see fifteen men employed in one field in 2000, whereas it was common in 1900.

the leases on the Weld estate insisted on a five-year rotation of crops, the use of artificial fertilisers, specified the number of livestock that could be kept, and encouraged efficient farming to ensure that the land was maintained 'in good heart'. All over the county, farm buildings were improved, land was drained and new methods were introduced.

Prominent among those who set out to provide an example of the best practice was the Revd. Anthony Huxtable at Sutton Waldron, where he was the rector from 1834 to 1871. He took over two local farms and proceeded to introduce modern methods, machinery and techniques, providing a model for neighbouring farmers. He used steam engines, pumped liquid manure to his fields, drained heavy land, and provided winter housing for his cattle and sheep. His experiments with crops, crop rotation and livestock attracted great attention, and not a few criticisms. Some were quick to point out that Huxtable was a rich man who could afford the large capital investment required. Nonetheless he established a national reputation as a leading exponent of 'high farming', publicising his work through the *Journals* of the Bath and West Society and the Royal Agricultural Society. Another 'example' farm was established at Bradford Abbas by Thomas Buckman (1814-1884) who had been a professor at the Cirencester Agricultural College. Buckman demonstrated how the new scientific discoveries could be applied to agriculture, and was an enthusiast for artificial fertilisers, careful crop rotation and for the cultivation of swede turnips as cattle food. He also wrote regularly in the farming journals and lectured to farmers' clubs throughout Dorset.

The availability of new implements and machinery, as well as steam power, played a major part in revolutionising farming in Dorset. Threshing machines, seed drills, winnowing and chaff-cutting machines, and the new metal ploughs, harrows, rollers and cultivators spread rapidly, especially on the larger farms, from the 1840s. The pressure for ever greater efficiency and productivity led to a renewed campaign for enclosures, and a massive extension of cultivation on to the downlands. Between 1800 and 1870 the land in more than fifty parishes in Dorset underwent enclosure by Act of Parliament. For example in 1824-7 more than 2,000 acres at Tarrant Hinton were enclosed, including the former open arable fields and the downland grazing. The whole landscape was changed, and the surviving very large enclosure map shows the ancient fields and the scattered strips of the tenants with the proposed new fields superimposed upon them, while a forty foot wide strip was provided for the Salisbury to Blandford road through the parish, and other new roads 30 feet wide were laid out to provide access to the new enclosures.

In 1861 600 acres at Winterborne Steepleton were enclosed by Act of Parliament, including the East, West and Middle arable fields, the Cow Leaze and the Sheep Down. The principal beneficiaries were the Duke of Clevedon, the Earl of Sandwich, Francis Henry Lambert of Dorchester and the rector, the Revd. Martin Johnson Green. Here, as elsewhere, although the allotment of land was scrupulously fair, the smaller holders found their new enclosures uneconomic and the costs of fencing insupportable and sold out to the larger farmers. It would be interesting to know their reaction to the provision in the Act that three acres were to be set aside 'as an allotment to grow fuel for the use of the labouring poor of Winterborne Steepleton'. Most dramatic of all was the enclosure of Fordington in 1876 when after prolonged resistance the tenants were obliged to submit, as their leases were bought up by the Duchy of Cornwall, and 3,500 acres of open field surrounding Dorchester were finally enclosed.

The mid-nineteenth century also saw a dramatic transformation and final taming of the Dorset chalk downland. These large areas of open sheep grazing had for centuries been one of the features of

A steam plough being demonstrated at Stourpaine during the 1970s. Ploughs of this sort, attached by cables to steam engines, were used to break up much of the ancient grassland on the Dorset downs during the later nineteenth century.

Dorset which most impressed travellers. Now the downland was increasingly ploughed up and brought into cultivation. Writing in 1854 Louis H. Ruegg was enthusiastic for this development and wrote that: The extent to which the downs of Dorset have been broken up may, without exaggeration be set at thousands of acres . . . with infinite advantage to the landlord and the tenant . . . the face of the whole district between Bryanstone and Milton Abbey has been changed, and the former furze breaks and heaths are become as fine a district as the county presents. Chesilborne, once a sheet of downs, has been brought into excellent cultivation under Lord Rivers. Between Dorchester and Blandford there is scarcely a parish in which the downs have not been broken up . . .'.

Writing in the *Journal* of the Bath and West Society in 1861, Joseph Darby, a Dorset farmer, wrote that, 'The chalk hills formerly presented to view one vast sheet of downs; cultivation was confined to the valleys . . . but what a change has been effected in their appearance'. In another article written in 1872 Joseph Darby again described the dramatic effects of this extension of cultivation on to the downland, and the many miles of new hedgerows which had been planted. But he regretted the destruction of so much archaeological evidence, and wrote that 'the ancient landmarks are obliterated'. On Cranborne Chase the numerous herds of deer were destroyed and some 4,000 acres brought into cultivation, following an Act of Parliament in 1828.

Much of the work of breaking up the downland was undertaken by steam ploughs. A large, heavy plough directed by a steersman was pulled across a piece of downland by a stout cable attached to two steam engines, one at each side of the ploughed area, each equipped with a winding drum. The system was introduced to Dorset during the 1860s, but reached its fullest extent after Francis Eddison established his Steam Ploughing Works at Dorchester in 1870. Eddison's double-engined plough sets were hired for work all over the county.

The livestock and dairy farmers of north and west Dorset were also greatly affected by the nineteenth-century developments. As well as the effect of the railways in opening up a new market for liquid milk,

A traditional milking scene at Horn Hill Dairy, Beaminster, in about 1911. The method and time-consuming nature of the work had scarcely changed over the centuries, and here, as on many Dorset diary farms, the breeds of cow remained very mixed.

A Dorset Down ram lamb. The breed was developed during the nineteenth century as part of the intense interest in improved livestock characteristics.

the demand for butter, cheese, pork, eggs and poultry continued to grow, and the reputation of Dorset products remained high. Early inventories and other documents rarely give any details about the variety or colour of the livestock listed, but traditionally Dorset cows had been a mixed breed of Longhorns, red cattle from Devon, white-faced Herefords and black cattle from Wales. Little attention was paid to selective breeding, and in 1815 William Stevenson wrote in *The General View of the Agriculture of Dorset* that 'There is no select breed of cattle in this county . . . and more regard is paid to the quantity of milk they are likely to produce, than to any other quality'.

The mid-nineteenth century saw the introduction of the dual-purpose Shorthorn which rapidly replaced earlier breeds and crosses, just as in the twentieth century the Friesian has become, by far, the most common dairy cow. By 1850 more than half the cattle in the county were Shorthorns or Shorthorn crosses. Ayrshires were also introduced and the Channel Island breeds which were imported

"Vaccar"

The
Only
Successful
Milker.

GOLD
MEDAL
THE
HAGUE.
1913.

Winner
numerous
Trials
and
Awards.

Machines to Milk One or Two Cows at a Time.

The Machine that has Established Faith in Mechanical Milking.

An advertisement for an early twentieth-century milking-machine.
An example was exhibited at the Dorchester Show in 1872, but
only after the 1939-45 war did they become the normal method of milking.

through Poole and Weymouth were adopted, especially on the home farms of some of the estates. Large numbers of fat cattle and pigs were produced and sent to the markets at Shaftesbury, Sturminster Newton and Salisbury, or were driven directly to Poole, Portsmouth or to Smithfield market in London. The traditional horned breed of Dorset sheep also faced stiff competition from new breeds, especially from the South Down and the Hampshire Down, which were distinguished by larger growth and early maturity. Eventually a distinctive Dorset Down breed was developed. The improved Dorset Horn, with its characteristic of early lambing and the production of twins, continued to be popular with many farmers, and a Dorset Horn Association was founded and a Herd Book established by the end of the century.

An indication of the developments which had occurred in Dorset farming can be found in the catalogue of the Bath and West Show which was held in Dorchester in 1872. The well-attended show lasted for five days, and the exhibitions by manufacturers and local agents

A traditional ploughing scene at Higher Kingston, Stinsford, during the
early twentieth century. Apart from the introduction of iron ploughs and
improved breeds of horses, the speed and technique of this essential
operation had not changed for over a thousand years.

included steam ploughs, threshing machines, reapers, drills, elevators,
ploughs and cultivators. There were demonstrations of all the newest
equipment, including an early version of a milking machine. Seeds
were available from Suttons of Reading, Carters of London and
Dunn's Farm Seeds of Gillingham. The latter had been founded by
Shadrach Dunn (1799-1867) at Gillingham in 1832. It had prospered
by specialising in good quality grass and clover seed, especially in
carefully-selected strains of the local marl-grass clover, a broadleaf red
clover. There were displays of farm produce and a formidable range of
livestock classes. The number of new and improved breeds of cattle,
sheep, pigs and poultry exhibited at the show was a remarkable
testimony to the work of breeders during the previous half century,
providing visible proof of the prosperity of Dorset agriculture.

The *Journal* of the Bath and West Society produced for the show a
long article on Dorset farming. This stressed the high standards, the
modern methods and the great increase in the cultivated area. It
described the large-scale use of artificial fertilisers and manufactured

Ox teams ploughing at Dewlish in about 1911. Oxen provided a strong, steady pull on the plough, and continued to be used throughout the nineteenth century, especially on heavy land. Horses were faster, and could work a longer day, and as breeds improved they gradually replaced oxen.

feedstuffs for livestock, the continuing importance of the water meadows, and the increasing size of farms, especially on the chalk. The average size of a Dorset farm was 88 acres, but some farms around Lulworth were said to be more than 1000 acres. A few farms on the chalk downland between Blandford and Wimborne were more than 1000 acres. The practice of renting cows to a dairyman continued, though the price had risen to as much as £12 per annum for each cow. As well as the despatch of liquid milk by the railways, most dairymen produced Cheddar cheese 'sufficiently good to pass off as Cheddar'. The cultivation of hemp and flax in west Dorset had declined greatly in the face of cheap imports from Russia and Scandinavia.

The mid-Victorian period was also a golden age for landowners, and the large estates in Dorset enjoyed an unparalleled prosperity. The extent to which landownership in Dorset was concentrated into a few hands was demonstrated by the enquiry into the ownership of land made by the order of Parliament and published in 1874. For the first time since the Domesday Survey of 1086 precise figures were available concerning the possessions of landowners, the size of their estates and their rental income. Thirty-six per cent of Dorset was occupied by nine great estates, each of more than 10,000 acres, and a further eighteen per cent by estates of 3,000 to 10,000 acres in extent. A further seventeen per cent comprised estates of 1,000 to 3,000 acres. The returns show that just over 100 people owned more than 70% of Dorset, while less than 7% of the county was held by owners of under 100 acres, a much lower figure than for most English counties.

Many Dorset landowners held large estates in other counties, but the ten largest estates within the county, together with the principal residence and the rental income, according to the 1874 Return were as follows:

Landowner	Principal Residence	Acreage	Annual Income
Major General Fox-Pitt-Rivers	Rushmore	24,942	£33,682
George Digby Wingfield-Digby	Sherborne	21,230	£36,106
Walter Ralph Bankes	Kingston Lacy	19,228	£14,985
Lord Wimborne	Canford Manor	17,400	£17,543
Earl of Shaftesbury	Wimborne St Giles	17,317	£12,536
Earl of Ilchester	Melbury	15,981	£18,515
Reginald Joseph Weld	Lulworth Castle	15,478	£13,704
John Samuel Wanley Sawbridge-Erle-Drax	Charborough Park	15,069	£11,631
Lord Alington	More Crichel	14,756	£21,140
Lord Stalbridge	Motcombe House	13,556	£31,409

These figures from the 1874 Return show the landowners at the height of their wealth, power and influence. The rise in rents had brought a considerable increase in their income, and many, like the Portmans, the Grosvenors (Lord Stalbridge), the Guests (Lord Wimborne), the Cecils (Marquess of Salisbury) and the Russells (Duke of Bedford) had sources of vast income elsewhere.

The effect of the dominance of great estates in the county is still evident. The great mansions and spreading parkland remain as characteristic landscape features in the county. Landowners also provided schools, churches, estate cottages and almshouses in villages throughout the county.

Sadly, the mid-Victorian prosperity of the landowners and tenant farmers was not shared by the labourers. The evidence of numerous observers, parliamentary reports and royal commissions bears witness to the wretched lives of many labourers, working long hours with low wages and living in grossly-overcrowded and inadequate cottages. A Parliamentary Report of 1843 shows that female labour was common in the fields and that children were often employed from the age of seven or eight. In 1867 a Commissioner reported that 'the proportion of boy labour regularly employed upon farms is larger than in any county visited by me.' He also observed that the cottages were very bad. 'The estate of Lord Rivers . . . is notorious for bad cottages. And such villages as Bere Regis, Fordington, Winfrith, Cranborne or Charminster (in which there is an average of seven persons to a house) . . . are a disgrace to the owners of the land and contain many cottages unfit for human habitation'. Some good estate cottages had been built, for example on Lord Shaftesbury's estate at Wimborne St Giles, by the Duke of Bedford at Swyre and by Lord Portman at Durweston and Pimperne, but most remained poor and the most elementary sanitation was totally lacking. The plight of the Dorset farm labourers was brought to national attention during the 1840s by a series of letters to *The Times* newspaper from Sidney Godolphin Osborne (known as S.G.O.), the well-connected and influential rector of Durweston.

Dorset lacked industries which might have provided alternative and better-paid employment, so in the absence of competition wages remained low, often no more than 12 shillings a week. The gulf between the life-style of the labourers and that of the landowners was immense.

THE AGRICULTURAL DEPRESSION
1878–1914

For Dorset farmers the mid-Victorian period of prosperity and optimism came to an end during the late 1870s with the onset of a deep and prolonged slump in prices which was to continue until the outbreak of war in 1914. A series of harsh springs followed by unusually wet summers led to outbreaks of disease among livestock and to disastrously poor harvests, particularly in 1878 and 1879. These years of low grain yields coincided with a drop in corn prices caused by the influx of wheat and barley from the prairies of the United States and Canada. Farmers had feared the possible effects of the Corn Laws in 1846, but it was now that the full effects of the policy of Free Trade began to be felt. Wheat which had sold for 70 shillings per quarter (i.e. 4 cwts.) had fallen to 46 shillings per quarter by 1875 and was selling at 24 shillings by 1890.

The price of barley dropped by nearly 40 per cent over the same period. The 1880s also saw the beginning of the import of large quantities of frozen beef from Argentina and the United States; cheese, wool, mutton and lamb also arrived from Australia and New Zealand, and flax and hemp from the Baltic. All these products were at prices which substantially undercut home produce. The large farms of the Dorset chalklands were particularly badly affected by the slump in prices. More and more land went out of cultivation, and many farmers were unable to pay their rent. With the sheep flocks no longer in demand for folding on the arable, and with the price of wool and mutton dropping rapidly, the great sheep flocks which for centuries had been such a characteristic feature of the Dorset downs began to disappear. In 1875 there were 524,297 sheep on Dorset farms; by 1898 the number was down to 365,310 and in 1913 had fallen to 292,973. During these years many of the water meadows which had

A prize-winning beef cow in about 1910. This was long before dehorning became common, and the cow's long horns are tipped with brass ferrules. The owner is in the traditional dress of a well-to-do farmer of this period.

been such an important part of the 'sheep-corn husbandry' of Dorset were abandoned and rapidly became overgrown. Likewise the acreage of arable land in the county shrank from 238,000 in 1870 to 161,000 in 1913, while the acreage of permanent pasture rose by more than 70 per cent.

Inevitably landowners saw their income from rents decline steadily as more and more of their tenants were unable to pay the rent, and either demanded a reduction or gave up their farms. Only estate owners who were not dependent upon farm rents could maintain their lavish life-style. The Portmans with their lucrative London properties were even able to build the great mansion at Bryanston in the 1890s in spite of the recession, the Guest family at Canford could rely on their industrial income, and the Grosvenor family could live on their estate at Motcombe and Gillingham, supported by the income of their London ground rents. Most other landowners were not so fortunate. Farm rents in Dorset fell by more than 30 per cent between 1870 and 1913, and even so more than a fifth of farmers gave up their farms during these years and it became increasingly difficult to find tenants.

In 1894 the government appointed a Royal Commission to inquire into the agricultural depression, and one of the assistant commissioners, Henry Rew, was sent to Dorset to collect evidence. His report, which was produced in 1895, gives a thoroughly bleak picture of the state of farming in Dorset. He concluded that 'it is impossible to view the situation in Dorset as a whole without gloomy forebodings of the immediate future of agriculture'; he also stated 'The ownership of land is rapidly becoming a luxury which only men possessing other sources of income can enjoy'. In support of this he cited figures showing the way in which the rent of farms had declined. Rent reductions between 1879 and 1895 had ranged from 25 to 30 per cent. A farm of 600 acres near Dorchester which had been let in 1855 for £517 per annum was let in 1895 for £220 per annum. Rew attended a meeting of farmers at Bere Regis which passed a resolution that, 'The farming of arable land has become absolutely unprofitable on account of the low price of produce'. In the light of his travels through the county, and having met many farmers, Rew summed up the situation:

'Some of the best and most substantial – and in times past the most successful – farmers in the south of England were to be found in Dorset, but with the present outlook it appears that the race is likely

The milk-collecting depot at Okeford Fitzpaine. It was the increasing demand for liquid milk and the improved means of transport which enabled most Dorset farmers to survive the late nineteenth-century agricultural depression.

to die out. Many hang on but cannot obtain a fair return on their capital. Capital is surely and steadily leaving the land'.

Never before had farmers faced such a sharp and prolonged recession and few could have imagined that prices would fall so low or that the flood of imported foodstuffs could have been so vast. By 1900 even the food sold to the wives of farmers and labourers in the village shops of Dorset was of foreign origin - Danish butter and bacon, tinned meat from North and South America, sheep meat from Australia and New Zealand, Canadian Cheddar cheese and bread made from flour grown on the North American prairies. The solutions to their problems proposed by Dorset farmers still remain matters of current debate. They suggested reform of the currency to reduce the price advantage of imported foodstuffs, protective tariffs for home-produced food, clear labelling of imported goods and cheaper freight charges on the railways.

The consequences of the agricultural depression were to be seen throughout Dorset in run-down farm buildings, abandoned arable land, neglected hedges and ditches, bracken-infested downland and overgrown water meadows. With the decline in arable farming, the number of men employed on the farms also dropped sharply and the number of farm labourers in Dorset fell from 16,000 in 1871 to 11,000 by 1901. All the trades which depended upon farming were also badly affected. The railways now made it possible for labourers and their families to leave and seek work in the industrial towns, while many others took the opportunities which were offered for assisted emigration. The effect of this 'drift from the land' was a substantial decline in the population of almost every village in the county.

THE TRADE IN LIQUID MILK

The desperate situation of many Dorset farmers was only relieved by one bright feature. This was the growing demand for liquid milk to supply the towns and the rapidly-growing resorts of Bournemouth and Weymouth. The population of Bournemouth climbed from 691 in 1851 to 78,674 by 1911; the twin resorts of Weymouth and Melcombe Regis grew from 8,000 to 12,000 over the same period, while both places welcomed a growing stream of summer visitors.

The Balch family and their dairy staff at Slodbrook Farm, Milton-on-Stour in about 1920. Note the typical cheese press, curd breakers and the samples of butter and cheese. One daughter, Hilda Balch, had a National Diploma for instructing in butter and cheese making throughout Dorset.

The milking team at Barton Farm, Cerne Abbas in about 1910. The ready market for liquid milk which was rapidly transported to urban dairies by the railways proved to be the salvation of many Dorset farms during the years of intense agricultural depression in the face of foreign imports.

Liquid milk was a product which remained immune from foreign competition, and demand grew steadily; while the railways provided a swift and efficient way of transporting it. More and more farmers turned to milk production and the number of cattle kept in the county soared from 75,000 in 1873 to nearly 100,000 by 1913. On countless Dorset farms the drive to the railway station with the milk churns became a daily routine. A collection depot for milk was established on the railway at Semley as early as 1871 and this was soon followed by others at Chard, Crewkerne, Yeovil, Wincanton, Stalbridge, Gillingham and Sturminster Marshall, from where milk was collected by the major dairy companies for dispatch to London and other large towns. The depot at Bailey Gate, Sturminster Marshall, on the now-abandoned railway line was for many years one of the major centres for the dispatch of milk along the whole of the south coast. Soon these milk depots were followed by factories for producing condensed milk, dried milk products and cheese, for example at Beaminster, Lydlinch and Yeovil. The Blackmore Vale cheese factory at Lydlinch was started in 1891 by a group headed by Wingfield Digby Esq; by 1895 it was using 1,200 gallons of milk each day, delivered twice daily by farmers. The cheese was sent to London via Stalbridge.

Apart from the dairy side, the general picture of Dorset farming at the end of the nineteenth century was one of contraction, unprofitability and unceasing struggle. The small family-run dairy farms without high labour costs, managed to survive, as did some of the largest and most efficient farms. When the novelist H. Rider Haggard visited Dorset in 1901 he was impressed by the large farming enterprise run by the Tory family, whose farms occupied much of the Winterborne valley from Turnworth to Winterborne Clenston and spread for several miles across the surrounding downland. He praised the excellence of their sheep flocks, especially the Dorset Downs, and the fine crops of high-quality barley. He was also full of admiration for the Portman estate farms and for the home farm at Bryanston where 'everything is managed without thought of cost'.

At the other end of the social scale, a successful experiment in providing smallholdings was conducted at Rew Farm, Martinstown, by the wealthy banker and landowner Sir Robert Edgcumbe. In 1888 he purchased the farm of 343 acres for £5,050, and divided it into 30 lots ranging from fi to 31 acres. These were then offered for sale as smallholdings on easy terms and were eagerly sought after. By 1895 Sir Robert Edgcumbe had been repaid all but £600 of his original outlay. The new owners erected dwellings or shacks, built glass houses, kept cows, pigs and poultry, and grew fruit and vegetables for sale in Weymouth and Dorchester. Not all of the enterprises proved to be successful, and some of the buildings were insubstantial and unsightly, but in general the experiment fulfilled the intentions of its founder. Within a few years the population supported by the land at Rew Farm had grown from 20 to over 100 people.

SOME SUCCESSES

A Dorset estate which was immune to the rigours of the depression because of the injection of finance made through commerce was Iwerne Minster. In 1876 it was purchased by Lord Wolverton, the son of a wealthy banker. He was a politician who from 1857 to 1873 was the Liberal M.P. for Shaftesbury. When he died in 1887 his personal estate was valued at £1,820,000 and he was well able to be a model landlord at Iwerne Minster where he built the large mansion, Clayesmore House, laid out a park of 150 acres, and contributed to the restoration of the church and the building of the village school.

In 1902 the estate of 3,000 acres at Iwerne Minster was purchased by another wealthy man, James Ismay. He had retired from the White Star Shipping Line of Liverpool at the age of 35, and until his death in 1930 devoted much of his large fortune to carrying out his ideas concerning agriculture and village life at Iwerne Minster. He built new farm houses, barns, stock-housing and dairies, provided eighty new cottages for labourers and in 1921 provided the large village club as the social centre of the village. He encouraged farming innovation of all sorts, cooperating with the Rothamsted Experimental Station in the trials of new varieties of crops and grasses, and introducing noted herds of Dairy Shorthorns, Berkshire and Middle White pigs and a flock of Hampshire Down sheep. He also set up a poultry farm and a bacon factory. Although obviously supported by his own great wealth derived from other sources, his enterprises proved to be a valuable

Harvesting watercress at Hooke in 1920. The clear streams of Dorset were ideal for the cultivation of this crop, and the railways provided rapid transport to urban markets. Note that in 1920 the wellington boot had not yet become the normal footwear, even for those working in water.

example to his tenants, as well as to landowners and farmers throughout central Dorset.

A hopeful sign amid the general gloom of the agricultural depression was the slow advances in crop and livestock breeding, and the introduction of new strains and new blood lines, providing greater productivity and disease resistance. In Wiltshire, E. S. Beaven (1857-1941) produced two new varieties of high-yielding barley, 'Plumage' and 'Archer' which were widely grown in Dorset during the twentieth century. In 1910 R.H. Biffen (1874-1949) produced in Cambridge his famous stiff-strawed and rust-resistant wheat, 'Little Joss', which soon became the most popular wheat in the country. A major local contribution to plant-breeding came from James Clark (1825-90), a gardener from Christchurch which was then in Hampshire. From the 1870s he began the lengthy and painstaking work of cross-pollinating potatoes and growing new varieties from the resulting seed. In 1876 he produced the blight-resistant 'Magnum Bonum' which was marketed by Suttons of Reading and for several years became the leading main-crop variety. It was to be one of the parents of the famous 'King Edward' variety. In 1876 Clark also produced 'Maincrop'; later a russet-skinned variant of this potato was to achieve great popularity under the name 'Golden Wonder'. Another of Clark's successful introductions was 'Epicure' (1897) a hardy, frost-resistant and heavy cropping potato which was to be grown throughout the country for many years, and was used in the parentage of other varieties, most notably 'Sutton's Foremost'. The numerous other varieties bred by Clark included 'Clark's Aristocratic Kidney', 'Clark's Cranemoor', 'Reading Hero', 'Sutton's Abundance', 'Matchless' and 'Nonesuch'.

THE TWENTIETH CENTURY

The decades following the outbreak of war in 1914 have seen more profound and far-reaching changes in farming and in rural life than any other period in the long history of Dorset agriculture. The greatly increased demand for home-produced foodstuffs during the First World War revived the prosperity of farming, boosted the production of cereals, livestock, milk and cheese, and stimulated the introduction of machinery. As war-time prices rose, arable land was extended, renewed emphasis was placed on obtaining maximum production, and the years of depression and 'survival' farming were replaced by a new optimism. The creation and extension of military and naval bases, especially at Portland and Poole, as well as at various places across the downlands such as the naval camp at Tarrant Launceston, increased

Churning butter at the Blackmore Vale Creamery during the early twentieth century.

Some of the horses lined up for sale at Abbotsbury in 1923. Many farmers
were forced to abandon their farms in the depression that followed the
end of the war in 1918.

the local demand for farm produce. Later, the establishment of several
prisoner-of-war camps created both a market for foodstuffs and a
supply of labour for farms. The Board of Agriculture, Ministry of
Food, and Dorset War Agricultural Executive Committee between
them ensured that farming was regulated and supervised as never
before, with guaranteed prices, minimum wages and the enforcement
of cultivation orders.

The revival in the fortunes of Dorset agriculture did not last long
after the end of the war in 1918. As with the years after the end of the
Napoleonic War in 1815, a prolonged depression followed the end of
hostilities. The 1920s saw a return to reliance on supplies of cheap,
imported food. Moreover, the effects of the war, followed by high
taxation and especially death duties, hit the owners of great estates
particularly hard, and there was a flood of land sales. Landowners
found that the income which could be earned from land represented a
much poorer return on capital than could be obtained from almost
any other investment. In 1918 Lord Alington sold a large part of his
estate at More Crichel, his heir having tragically died on Armistice
Day 1918, after being seriously wounded at the beginning of the War.
Lord Wimborne sold Canford in 1922. Despite their vast wealth, the
Portmans left Bryanston House which had been built at such great
expense in 1889-94, and it later became a school. Outlying parts of

An early demonstration of tractor-drawn ploughing at Look Farm, Puncknowle in about 1910. Like steam-powered ploughs, the first generation of tractor ploughs required a ploughman or steersman to control the depth and maintain a straight course. The tractor is a rare example made by Allday and Onions, one of several early twentieth century makers of whom the best known were the Ivel and Saunderson companies.

the Digby estate and the lands of the Marquess of Anglesey were sold, while many of the institutional landowners such as colleges at Oxford, Cambridge, Winchester and Eton put their Dorset lands on the market.

During the years 1918-22 a quarter of the land of England changed hands in a transfer of ownership not equalled since the dispersal of the former monastic lands in the sixteenth century. Even so, more estates survived in Dorset than in many other counties. Many of the farms in Dorset were purchased by sitting tenants, greatly increasing the number of owner-occupiers in the county. After 1918 the price of wheat and barley fell rapidly and the area of arable land in Dorset declined until by 1929 only 16 per cent of the available land was ploughed. Sheep numbers continued to fall, and farmers depended once more on milk production and the raising of livestock for their livelihood. Falling profits and increasing costs of labour meant that fewer people were employed on farms, and the population of many Dorset villages continued to decline.

A development of the inter-war years which did much to alleviate the traditional isolation and loneliness of many women living on the often remote and solitary farms of Dorset was the establishment of Women's Institutes throughout the county. One of the first to be founded was at Wallisdown in 1915; others followed rapidly and soon became important in the social life of villages as well as providing new insights and information about modern developments in health, hygiene, domestic concerns and labour-saving ideas for the home. In the same way the social life of many young people living on farms was improved by the establishment of Young Farmers' Clubs which provided education, competitions and social occasions. They also soon became a major force in bringing potential marriage partners together.

The spread of 'council houses' provided by Rural District Councils during the 1920s and 1930s introduced a higher standard of housing into many villages, while the provision of improvement grants from 1926 brought piped water, damp-proofing and better sanitation for some rural workers. Most rural households, however, remained without electricity until the late 1930s and even later. Tied cottages continued to be the normal accommodation for workers on many farms. Standards often remained poor, although rents were likewise low. A few estates provided much improved housing, notably the cottages built by Sir Ernest Debenham at Briantspuddle and by James Ismay at Iwerne Minster.

Although price controls were removed at the end of the war in 1918, Government intervention in all aspects of agriculture and rural life did not cease. An early example was the creation in 1919 of the Forestry Commission, which was responsible for planting large areas of the Dorset heath with fast-growing conifers, greatly altering the distinctive landscape of that part of the county.

In spite of the general recession in the fortunes of agriculture, there were a few prosperous farming enterprises to be found in Dorset during the 1920s, although some depended upon capital provided by industrial or commercial activities elsewhere. The modern farming methods introduced on the estate at Iwerne Minster by James Ismay were mentioned in the previous chapter. The most remarkable example of the introduction of commercial capital into Dorset farming occurred at Briantspuddle. In 1914 Ernest Debenham used the wealth acquired from his London drapery stores to purchase and develop a

Some of the tractors and delivery vehicles in use on the Bladen Estate at Briantspuddle in 1929. The range of equipment in use on the estate shows the application of modern methods and the capital investment provided by Ernest Debenham.

model 3,000 acre estate centred on Briantspuddle and including a large area of the adjacent parishes along the Piddle valley. This enterprise was known as Bladen Farms, and set out to show how the application of scientific techniques could produce profitable farming and revive the most attractive features of rural life. High-quality pedigree livestock were introduced, and the associated operations included a milk-processing factory, a corn-mill, brick-works, saw-mill and lime-kiln. The arable land grew wheat, oats, swede turnips, kale, vetch and Italian rye-grass, all of which were cultivated according to the latest scientific principles. Visitors were welcomed, and Debenham wrote that his chief object was to show that it was possible profitably to produce home-grown foodstuffs and at the same time to reverse rural depopulation, the 'drift from the land', and to make rural life agreeable by providing good housing and a variety of communal activities. During Debenham's lifetime his experiment was undoubtedly successful and in 1931 he was created a baronet for his services to agriculture. Without his wealth, however, it could never have been started, and sadly, after his death in 1952 the estate was broken up and the farms were sold.

Another attempt to revive both agriculture and traditional rural life in Dorset also became nationally famous during the 1930s. This was the farming community founded at Fontmell Magna by the idealist Rolf Gardiner (1902-71) who, in 1927, inherited from his uncle the Springhead estate stretching across the downs between Shaftesbury and Blandford Forum. He wished to bring young people from different backgrounds and different countries together, including the youth of Britain and Germany which had so recently fought a bloody and destructive war. He instituted international work-camps, music, drama, folk-song and dancing with farm work, the reclamation of derelict land and the afforestation of steep downland hillsides. He also introduced ideas of organic farming and self-sufficiency. Among other experiments he planted orchards, set up local food-processing industries and re-introduced flax-growing to west Dorset, reviving a flax-mill at Slape near Netherbury. His activities, both agricultural and cultural, attracted a great deal of interest, but some of his ideas were

Flax being harvested near Bridport. Flax-growing was revived in west Dorset by Rolf Gardiner. During the 1939-45 war, flax was in demand for the manufacture of fire-fighting hoses.

derived from the German youth movement, and the involvement of young people from Germany brought him considerable adverse criticism, especially after the Nazi movement came to power during the later 1930s.

With the abolition of guaranteed prices during the inter-war years, farmers' incomes fell, and many Dorset farmers reverted to the pre-war policy of survival by reducing expenditure to a minimum. Maintenance of buildings, hedges and equipment was neglected, the purchase of artificial fertilisers and processed cattle feed was reduced. Cheap fences of posts and barbed wire were increasingly used on the downland, despite the opposition of local hunts. Wide mesh wire-netting replaced hurdles for sheep folds. Wages for farm workers in Dorset, which had risen to as much as £1 or even £1 10s 0d a week during the period 1914-18, fell again, especially after the depression which began in 1929. Only on the largest farms was modern machinery introduced; horses remained the main providers of motive power on most Dorset farms. Few farmers would afford the expense of a tractor. In 1935 a new Fordson with straked wheels or 'spade-lugs' and running on paraffin cost £140, and pneumatic tyres cost an extra £40. In total this was more than the price of a pair of horses. The introduction of the convenient Ferguson tractor with its highly-successful hydraulic system increased the popularity of tractors for smaller farms, but by the outbreak of war in 1939 there were still less than 1,000 tractors used for farm work in Dorset, and on most farms the horses and horsemen still reigned supreme.

Many farmers remained almost totally reliant on the trade in liquid milk. More than half of the cattle kept in the county were dairy cows, mostly Dairy Shorthorns. Few dairy farmers bred their own stock, selling calves and relying on heifers imported from Wales and Ireland for replacements. On the well-drained downland bail milking became popular during the 1920s. This was a system evolved by A.J. Hosier in Wiltshire which used a portable milking parlour which could be towed to any part of the downland. In conjunction with a piped water supply and a stationary oil-engine, a complete dairy with a milking machine could be used at places remote from farmsteads, and could be moved at will, dispensing with the need for expensive buildings.

A Fordson Major tractor with three-furrow plough. The hydraulic lift system being used here had been introduced by Harry Ferguson in 1934, using the power of the engine to lift the plough out of the ground. This scene from about 1960 shows the plough equipped with three-point linkage, disc coulters and a large 'land wheel' to control the depth.

CHANGES SINCE 1939

The renewed pressure for the maximum food production during the Second World War and thereafter, and the massive changes brought about by the application of scientific techniques to all aspects of farming, have brought further remarkable changes to Dorset farming. The true 'agricultural revolution' has occurred since 1939. The wartime conditions of 1939-45 saw government intervention into farming and compulsion upon farmers as never before. The Dorset War Agricultural Executive Committee had powers to compel the break-up of grassland for crops and to enforce the cultivation of desperately needed crops. Subsidies, incentive schemes, acreage payments and

War-time ploughing for the first time on Manston Down, Winterborne Kingston in 1942. The slow, laborious work of horse-drawn ploughing with a single furrow plough remained the norm on many Dorset farms throughout the war years.

Self-propelled Massey Harris Combine Harvesters working on Crichel Down in 1950. Although they had long been in use on the American prairies, few combines were used in England until the Second World War. During the War the numbers in use rose rapidly, but even in 1950 it was unusual to see five working together.

assistance with mechanisation all hastened change. Labour was supplied by the Women's Land Army (the Land Girls) and later by prisoners of war. Tractors, combine harvesters, grain driers and milking machines all multiplied. By the end of the war in 1945 the number of farm horses in Dorset had fallen to about 5,000 while there were more than 4,000 tractors.

Threshing at Blackmarsh Farm, near Sherborne in 1956. This sort of steam-driven thresher and steam elevator, which had been common throughout Dorset since the mid-nineteenth century was soon to be almost completely replaced by the combine harvester.

These trends have continued with the rapid spread of electricity, piped water supplies, modern milking parlours, artificial insemination and the application of scientific methods to plant breeding, fertilisers, pesticides, fungicides and herbicides. Farm sizes have continued to increase through amalgamations and large-scale cereal production has replaced grassland over vast areas of the downs. In north and west Dorset dairy farming remains predominant. In 1958 there were 3,029 farms in Dorset, of which 2858 or 78 per cent were dairy farms. Working horses have almost completely disappeared from the land, and the labour force is tiny compared to the number employed a century ago. The great folding sheep flocks which were once a major characteristic of Dorset farming have disappeared. In their place are new crops such as oil-seed rape, maize and linseed. New techniques in silage-making, 'zero-grazing' and grassland cultivation have largely replaced the former importance of the hay-harvest as a source of winter feed, and have also superseded the early grass provided by the water meadows.

In 1949 Dorset County Council purchased the estate at Kingston Maurward and established a Farm Institute which in 1982 became the Dorset College of Agriculture. This has done much to spread knowledge of the latest developments and best practice. The present size of farms, the number of owner-occupiers, the complexity of farming operations, the controls on quality and prices exercised by outside agencies, the prodigious capital expenditure required for land, stock, buildings and machinery would be beyond the wildest dreams

This fully-automated and computerised milking parlour could not be more different from the dairies depicted in some of the earlier illustrations. The contrast is a measure of the revolution which agriculture has undergone in the twentieth century. This illustration shows the way in which the yield of each numbered cow is monitored and recorded; it also reveals the emphasis upon hygiene, and labour saving, as well as the large capital investment required.

A robust response to the latest crisis to afflict farming. It is a measure of the revolutionary improvement in yields, that the late nineteenth-century depression was caused by foreign foodstuffs, whereas this late twentieth-century protest is concerned with exports.

of a Dorset farmer in the Victorian period. Even a farmer from the inter-war years would be amazed at the increased power of tractors, the size and complexity of modern machinery, and at developments such as free-range pig units, specialised horticulture, intensive poultry and egg production, diversification into unusual crops and livestock, organic farming and the almost complete adoption of the Friesian as the supreme breed of dairy cow. All would be surprised at the large areas of former agricultural land devoted to military training or to holiday caravans, at the way in which redundant farm buildings have been turned into homes, at the inroads made into the heath and downland, and the disappearance of farms beneath the spread of towns and villages; and at government subsidies to encourage the growth of certain crops, and of 'set-aside' payments to restrict the cultivation of others. Also surprising is the widespread cultivation of 'new' crops such as maize, oil-seed rape, linseed, lupins and other alternative crops, and the raising of deer, bison, wild boar, ostriches and even alpacas.

Likewise, earlier farmers would be incredulous at the increases in agricultural productivity which have been achieved in the later twentieth century. This can be summed up in the figures for the three major products of Dorset farms. In 1900 wheat crops produced an average of 17.7 cwts. per acre, barley yielded 15.9 cwts. per acre, and 500-600 gallons was the average milk production of a dairy cow during each lactation. A century later all the modern changes which have just been summarised and the intensive application of scientific techniques and advances mean that a good average for wheat production can be as high as 3 tons or 60 cwts. per acre, barley can yield as much as 2 tons or 50 cwts. per acre, and a good dairy cow in a well-managed dairy will produce more than twice as much milk per lactation as her predecessor in 1900. Whatever opinion may be held about some modern developments or the long-term wisdom of some methods, these figures provide a dramatic measure of the scale of the twentieth-century agricultural revolution.

FURTHER READING

The volumes of the *Proceedings* of the Dorset Natural History and Archaeological Society and those of Somerset and Dorset Notes and Queries provide a vast amount of information on all aspects of farming and rural life in Dorset. There are also numerous books which deal wholly or in part with the subject. The following are some of the more recent publications:

Bettey, J. H., *Rural Life in Wessex*, 1977
Bettey, J. H., *Man & the Land: Farming in Dorset 1846-1996*, 1996
Burnett, D., *Dorset Camera 1855-1914*, 1974
Darby, H. C., *The Domesday Geography of South-West England*, 1967
Draper, Jo, *The Georgians*, 1998
Fowles, John & Draper, Jo, *Thomas Hardy's England*, 1984
Hearing, T., *The Dorset Horn*, 1990
Hinton, D., *Alfred's Kingdom, Wessex & the South 800-1500*, 1977
James, Jude, *The Victorians*, 1998
James, J. F. & Bettey J. H. eds., *Farming in Dorset: Diary of James Warne, 1758, Letters of George Boswell 1787-1805*, Dorset Record Society, 13, 1993
Kerr, B., *Bound to the Soil: A Social History of Dorset 1750-1918*, 1968
Lloyd, R., *Dorset Elizabethans*, 1967
Roberts, A. W. M., *Farming in Dorset*, 1980
Taylor, C., *The Making of the English Landscape: Dorset*, 1970
Whitlock, Ralph, *Dorset Farming*, 1982

ACKNOWLEDGEMENTS

Many of those to whom I am indebted for information are listed in the bibliography. I would also like to thank Jo Draper for reading earlier drafts and for her perceptive comments; and David Burnett for his careful editing. My daughter, Dr Mary Bettey provided information about James Clark and his potatoes. I am grateful for the assistance of the archivists at the Dorset Record Office in Dorchester and at the Salisbury Diocesan Record Office at Trowbridge.

I would like to thank the following for allowing the inclusion of illustrations in their possession or for which they hold the copyright. British Library: page 9 (top); Cambridge University Collection of Air Photographs: pages 8, 12, 13; Dorset Natural History and Archaeological Society: frontispiece, pages 31, 46, 49, 52, 53, 57, 60 (bottom), 63, 67, 72, 73 (both), 76; Dorset Record Office: pages 38, 39 (top), 69; Gillingham Museum: page 60 (top); Kings College, Cambridge: page 24; Jo Parsons: page 75; Royal Commission on Historical Monuments (England), © Crown copyright reserved: pages 17, 18; Sherborne Museum: page 74.

The

DISCOVER DORSET

Series of Books

A series of paperback books providing informative illustrated
introductions to Dorset's history, culture and way of life.
The following titles have so far been published.

All the books about Dorset published by The Dovecote Press
are available in bookshops throughout the county,
or in case of difficulty direct from the publishers.
The Dovecote Press Ltd, Stanbridge,
Wimborne, Dorset BH21 4JD
Tel: 01258 840549   www.dovecotepress.com